Usborne STEAM

INVENTIONS

Scribble Book

THE INVENTIONS IN THIS BOOK WERE SCRIBBLED BY:

Anika Shukla

Written by
**ALICE JAMES &
TOM MUMBRAY**

Illustrated by
PETRA BAAN

Designed by
**Emily Barden &
Samuel Gorham**

Series editor **Rosie Dickins**

Series designer **Zoe Wray**

Expert advice from
DR. DAVID ROONEY

CONTENTS

RISE AND SHINE!

Invent gadgets to wake you up...

...and send you to sleep.

Imagine inventions that can be reused again and again.

TOOT

Design your own musical instrument.

CRASH

BANG

Come up with something pointless...

What invention would you not want to live without?

WHAT IS AN INVENTION?

INVENTING is about BUILDING, CREATING or DESIGNING something to solve a problem or do something in a NEW WAY. People have been INVENTING things for thousands of years – from ancient stone tools to today's high-tech spaceships.

Some inventions have stood the test of time...

...some we don't see around so much today.

Wheels

Clocks

Chainmail

Sock suspenders

Money

Bridges

Cassette tapes

Some inventions have lasted, but have changed a lot over the years.

1880s

1930s

1980s

1990s

TODAY

Not all inventions are physical objects. Things like music, sports, puzzles and recipes are inventions too.

WHAT'S IN THIS BOOK?

This book is full of things to:

DESIGN

Imagine

CREATE

INVENT

BUILD

ANYONE can invent something. It just takes a little creativity to think up something NO ONE has thought of BEFORE.

WHAT WILL YOU NEED?

For most of the book, you'll only need your imagination and a pencil. Occasionally you might also need paper, glue, a ruler and scissors.

USBORNE QUICKLINKS

To download copies of the templates in this book, and for links to websites with more ideas, activities and inspiration for inventions, go to USBORNE.COM/QUICKLINKS and type in the keywords: 'scribble inventions'.

Please follow the online safety guidelines at the Usborne Quicklinks website. Children should be supervised online.

THINK LIKE AN INVENTOR

Inventors have to start by thinking hard about what people DON'T HAVE, but MIGHT NEED. What hasn't been invented yet, and how could it make life better? Then inventors bring their idea to LIFE.

Fill in these boxes to follow the journey of an idea. Use one of these ideas, or come up with your own.

A gadget that can work out what is making someone ill.

A machine that can wash a person and their clothes at the same time.

A container that stops food from going bad.

You could keep an inventor's notebook to jot down thoughts and ideas.

RESEARCH IT

Have a look online, or in books. Is your idea new, or are there similar inventions out there? How would you make yours different? Draw it below.

Time Machin

In

Out

DEVELOP IT

Think through your idea.
Draw diagrams and make notes.

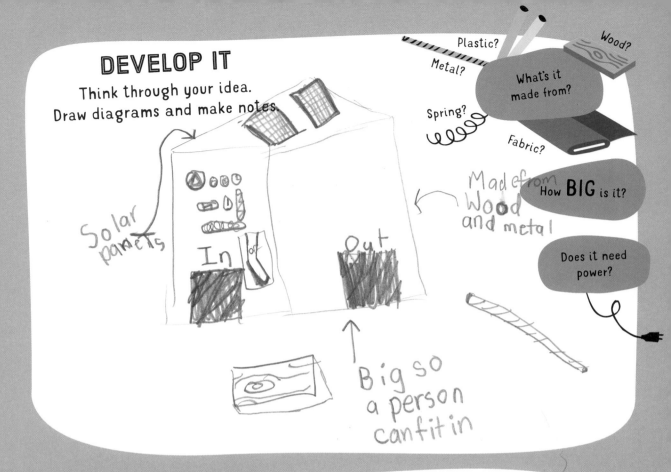

Plastic?

Metal?

Wood?

What's it made from?

Spring?

Fabric?

Solar panels

Made from Wood and metal

How **BIG** is it?

Does it need power?

In

Out

Out

Big so a person can fit in

DRAW IT OUT

Draw a final version of your invention here,
based on all your notes and diagrams above.

In

Out

The next stage for an inventor is to **BUILD** a model. Turn to page 48 to try it out.

PROBLEM FIXER

Try out some CREATIVE THINKING techniques to help you come up with new, problem-solving inventions. You can use the method that works best for you next time you're inventing something.

Choose one of the problems below or think of your own. Then use the following techniques to generate ideas for inventions that could solve the problem.

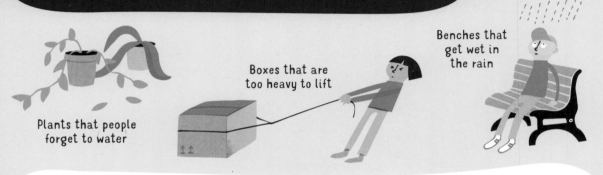

Plants that people forget to water

Boxes that are too heavy to lift

Benches that get wet in the rain

WORD CONNECTIONS

Focus on the KEY WORDS from your problem. Jot down any words they make you think of.

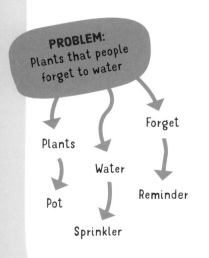

PROBLEM:
Plants that people forget to water

Plants → Pot

Water → Sprinkler

Forget → Reminder

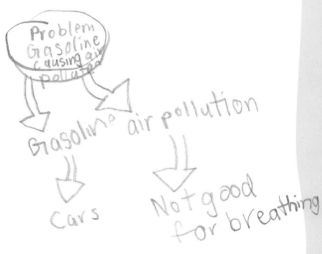

Problem Gasoline causing air pollution

Gasoline air pollution

Cars

Not good for breathing

See if any of the words spark ideas for inventions.

ANYTHING GOES

Scribble down EVERY idea you can think of to solve the problem.

Pipes that send drain water from sinks to plants

Smart pot that sets off an alarm when plants need watering

solar power cars

Instead of gas use water

Write down all your ideas WITHOUT worrying about how they would work.

WHAT IF?

Write down WHAT IF questions about your problem, then try answering them.

QUESTION:
WHAT IF plants could water themselves?

ANSWER:
Self-watering pot that automatically adds water when soil dries out

Q:-
What if you could pedal on pedals built inside the car so no gasoline?

Ans:-
you could pedal and the driver would stop and steer the car.

REFUSE, REUSE, RECYCLE

If you can't avoid plastic bags and bottles or cardboard by refusing them in the first place, then try reducing waste by inventing new ways to REUSE them.

A PLASTIC BAG

Plant pot

Toy parachute

Sail

← outside toilet

A PLASTIC BOTTLE

← Peanuts storer

Musical instrument

Piggy bank

Bird feeder

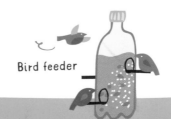

A CARDBOARD BOX

Clothes dresser

Pinhole camera

Portable
dog bed

Dress-up
costume

PUT IT ALL TOGETHER
Now try using ALL THREE items, or ANYTHING else that might be thrown away, to create something new. Let your imagination run wild...

HOW ABOUT...

...A SPACESHIP?

Cardboard box
cockpit

Plastic bag
sail

Plastic bottle
jetpacks

WAKE UP!

Most alarm clocks beep and buzz to wake people up. Design an alarm that works in a NEW way to get people out of bed in the morning.

IT COULD BE A...

Robot that wafts the smell of breakfast towards you

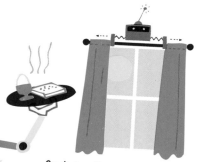

Curtains that automatically open, to wake you up with natural light

Alarm that monitors your sleep and goes off when you've had enough

RELAAAX

A lot of inventions are geared towards helping people to relax and switch off. Come up with your own soothing invention.

What kind of object is it?
- A blanket
- A piece of furniture
- A robot

Gives you a hug

What calming features does it have?
- Projects twinkly star-like lights
- Plays relaxing music
- Sprays soothing smells, such as lavender

DEEP-SEA DIVING

About 80% of the ocean is still unexplored. Scientists know a lot about shallow coral reefs and shores, but it's much harder to study things down in the deep...

DESIGN
a vehicle to go diving deep, deep under the sea.

NAME: SWIM 'N' SENSE
USE: Mapping the ocean
FEATURES: Sensors to work out where the seabed is

Propeller

Sensors

Bionic legs with flippers

Deep under the sea, the water overhead is extremely heavy. So ships have to be very strong to withstand the pressure.

Paddles for steering

If the vehicle has a crew, it will need a way to see out. Will you have portholes or is a whole section made of glass?

NAME: JEWEL QUEST 1,000
USE: Searching for hidden treasures
FEATURES: Metal detector to hunt for sunken ships or treasure

Grabber hand

Magnetic attachments to pick up sunken iron

Bubble jet engine

The deep ocean is pitch black. Make sure your vehicle has lights.

NAME: SUB-SEA SPECIES SPOTTER
USE: Finding new species
FEATURES: Video cameras to record sea creatures: instant species identifier

FROM FICTION TO REALITY

Writers sometimes come up with a fantastic gadget which is followed
later by a real-life version. Match each imaginary gadget
with the invention that followed it.

1. **STORY:** FAHRENHEIT 451
   AUTHOR: RAY BRADBURY
   YEAR: 1953
   INVENTION: Small wearable
   devices, used to listen to music
   and the radio

2. **STORY:** DICK TRACY
   AUTHOR: CHESTER GOULD
   YEAR: From 1946
   INVENTION: Gadgets worn on
   the wrists of police officers, which can
   share information with each other

3. **STORY:** LOOKING BACKWARD
   AUTHOR: EDWARD BELLAMY
   YEAR: 1888
   INVENTION: Cards punched with
   holes, to record the value of customers'
   purchases in shops

4. **STORY:** CYBORG
   AUTHOR: MARTIN CAIDIN
   YEAR: 1972
   INVENTION: Electronic body
   parts, to replace a pilot's injured
   limbs after a crash

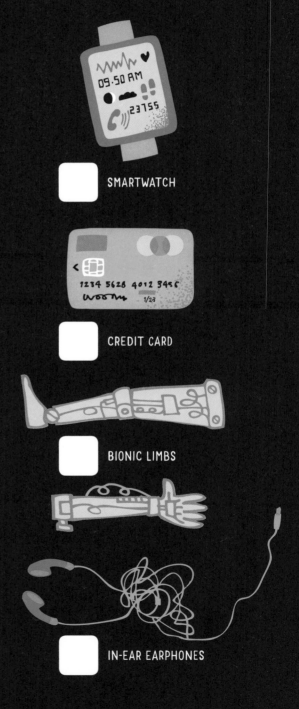

SMARTWATCH

CREDIT CARD

BIONIC LIMBS

IN-EAR EARPHONES

Imagine you're writing a story about an explorer
investigating a mysterious underground world.
Invent a device the explorer could use.

A suit with
features that
let the explorer
tunnel through
rocks

Glasses that can see
through solid rock

Headphones that
can pick up quiet
sounds in the dark

THERE'S AN APP FOR THAT

An app is a computer program that runs on a phone or tablet.
What app would you like to create? Invent it here.

WHAT IS YOUR APP FOR?

To play a game

To help with navigation

DOG SAVES THE DAY

To display news stories

To answer questions

THE FIRST QUEEN WAS...

HOW WILL PEOPLE USE IT?

QUESTION

Type answers to quiz questions while a timer ticks down

Drag letters to finish a puzzle

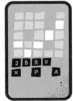

Draw and save a route across a map using a finger

HOW WILL IT LOOK?
Draw it on the tablet screen below.

Apps need an eye-catching image known as an icon, so they're easy to find.

NEWS ON THE MOVE

PUZZLE PLAYER

QUICK QUIZZES

Design your own icon here.

Give your app a catchy name and write it here.

DRAW IT OUT

Once you've come up with a design for an object, you can turn it into a TECHNICAL DRAWING. This means laying it out clearly and TO SCALE, making each part the right size compared to the rest.

Here's an example of a technical drawing.

Technical drawings are detailed and precise.

Inventor's sketch

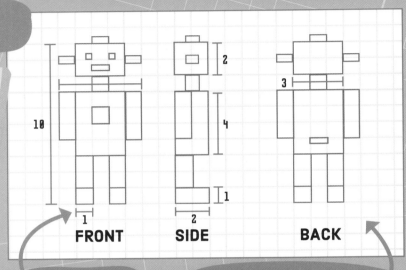

10

2

4

1

3

1   2

FRONT   **SIDE**   **BACK**

Measurements, known as **DIMENSIONS**, are included.

Each drawing shows a different view. Straight **GRIDLINES** help to make sure sizes stay the same between views.

Here's a rough inventor's sketch of a new **RADIO**. The inventor has added dimensions.

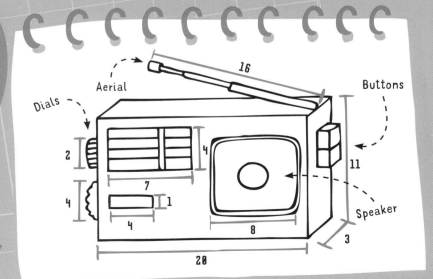

Aerial

16

Buttons

Dials

2

4

7

4

1

4

11

Speaker

8

3

20

20

Finish off the **FRONT** view of the inventor's radio, using the sketch on the left and the gridlines to help.

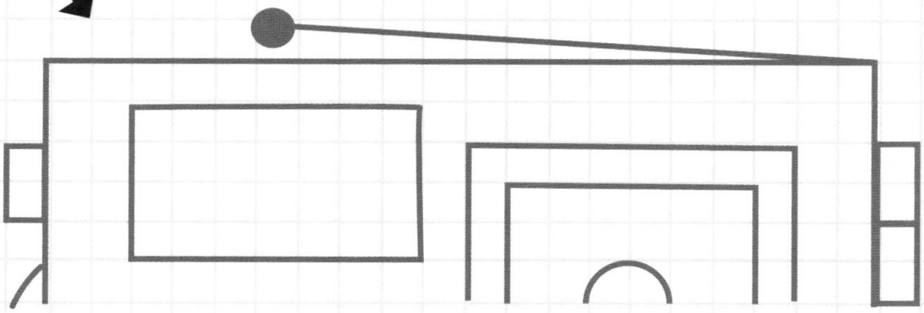

Pick a **SIDE** and draw that too. Put buttons or dials in the right places.

Now draw the **BACK**. Make sure the height and width are the same as the front.

The rough sketch doesn't show the back, so use your imagination to decide how it will look.

Draw the **TOP** here.

The top should be the same width as the sides.

Try turning one of your own inventions into a technical drawing here. It's best to start with an invention that has a fairly simple shape.

Use the gridlines to help create the basic shape. Then add the details.

Drawings like this are known as BLUEPRINTS, as they used to be done on blue paper. Today, most technical drawings are produced by computers.

PUT IT TOGETHER

Lots of inventions come from combining TWO IDEAS that already exist,
such as hats with headphones in them, or refrigerators with ice makers built in.

Pick any two items from the list
below - or think of your own - and
combine them to make something new.

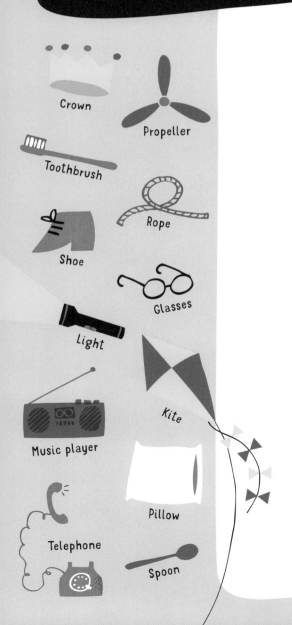

Crown

Propeller

Toothbrush

Rope

Shoe

Glasses

Light

Kite

Music player

Pillow

Telephone

Spoon

For more ideas, try using
the random invention
generator on the next page.

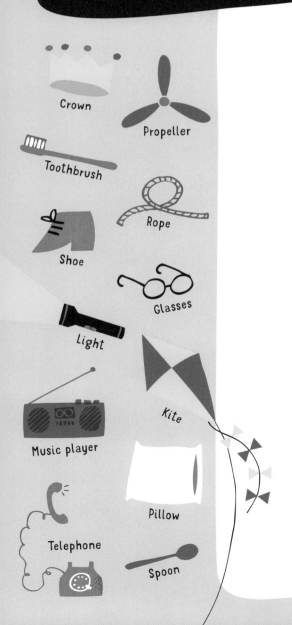

23

INVENTION GENERATOR

Very few inventions are entirely new. Take the car – wheels, engines and horse-drawn carriages all existed separately before they were combined to create cars.

WHEEL + ENGINE + CARRIAGE = CAR

If you're in need of some inspiration, try making this INVENTION GENERATOR. Flip through it to create different combinations of parts, then see what ideas these spark...

Copy the templates on the next two pages, or download them from the Usborne QUICKLINKS website.

1.

Cut along the solid black lines. Put the base strip and the top strip to one side.

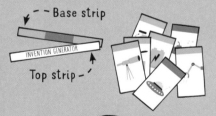

Base strip

INVENTION GENERATOR

Top strip

2.

Stack the remaining pieces of paper into three piles, according to whether they have an orange, blue or green end.

3.

Staple or clip all the orange pieces onto the orange part of the base strip.

Staple

4.

Repeat, stapling all the blue pieces onto the blue part of the base strip, and all the green pieces onto the green part.

5.

Finally, staple or clip the top strip on, like this.

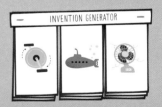

INVENTION GENERATOR

Now flip through and see what you come up with.

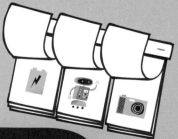

If you want to **DESIGN YOUR OWN** generator just turn it over and scribble a different power source, machine or attachment on each section.

This is the base strip.

This is the top strip.

INVENTION GENERATOR

...with a vacuum cleaner.

...with magnetic arms.

...robot...

...conveyor belt...

Battery-powered...

Water wheel-powered...

...with a fan.

...with nets.

...submarine...

...spaceship...

Pedal-powered...

Solar-powered...

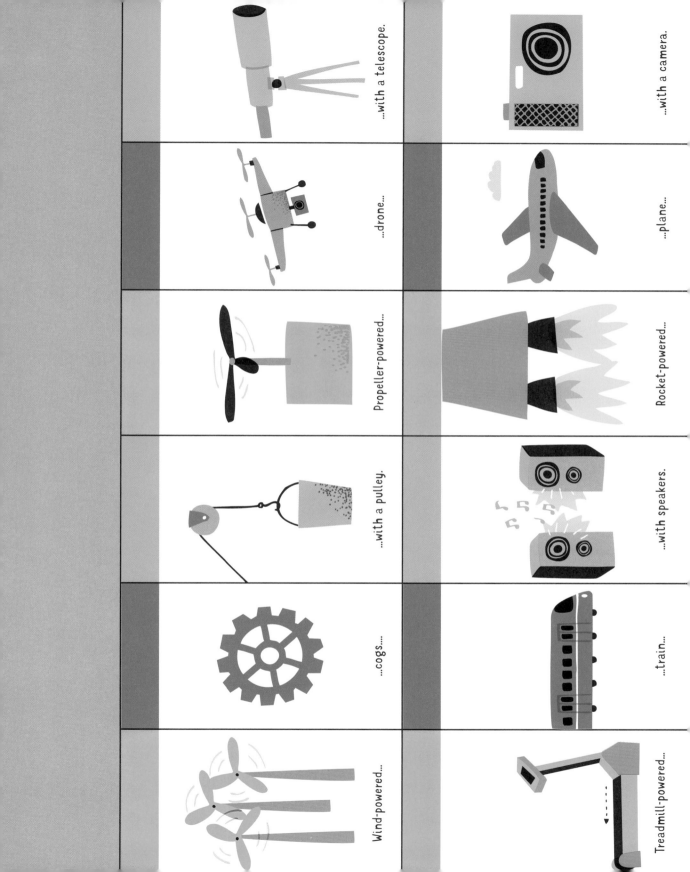

...with a telescope.

...with a camera.

...drone...

...plane...

Propeller-powered...

Rocket-powered...

...with a pulley.

...with speakers.

...cogs....

...train...

Wind-powered...

Treadmill-powered...

STAYING HEALTHY

From stethoscopes and thermometers to X-rays and robotic surgeons, MEDICAL INVENTIONS play a crucial role in keeping people healthy, and helping them to recover from illness.

IMAGINE a device to help people stay healthy.

A robot that cooks healthy, nutritious food

A machine that can check your temperature...

...then cools you down or warms you up

A t-shirt that records blood pressure and heart rate

EARLY INVENTIONS

The earliest inventors created all sorts of things using
only the materials they found around them,
such as wood, stones and plants.

Reeds

Long grasses

Clay

Shells

Sticks

Stones

DESIGN an invention using just the materials above. There are lots of ideas at the bottom.

TRANSPORTATION

Canoe made from
a hollowed-out
tree trunk

Raft made out of
logs and vines

Basket woven
from reeds

Vines

Leaves

Berries

Logs and branches

SHELTER

Leaves

Sticks

Bound with vines

TOOLS

Pots made from clay...

...painted with ground-up plants and berries

Sticks

Stones

Most instruments can make a range of sounds, from low to high.

HIGHER sounds are made by...

...**SMALLER** objects

...**SHORTER** tubes

...**SHORTER, TIGHTER** strings.

LOWER sounds are made by...

...**BIGGER** objects

...**LONGER** tubes

...**LONGER, LOOSER** strings.

XYLOPHONE

PAN PIPES

HARP

MAKE SOME NOISE

When objects move back and forth they create VIBRATIONS. These vibrations make SOUND.

Drums are HIT.

BANG

CRASH

Cymbals SMASH.

TOOT TOOT

Air BLOWS through a trumpet.

Metal makes a clanging sound when hit.

Guitar strings are PLUCKED or STRUMMED.

PLINK PLONK

Strings make a twanging sound when plucked.

TAP

Wood blocks SCRAPE.

Maracas SHAKE.

Can it make high and low sounds? How?

What's it made of?

How would it be played?

DESIGN YOUR OWN instrument here.
Use the instruments above for inspiration.

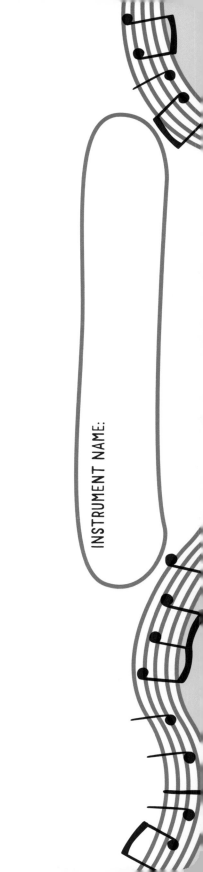

INSTRUMENT NAME:

WORKING WITH WHEELS

Wheels have been around for 5,000 years, first of all for potters to spin clay, later for vehicles, and all sorts of other things too...

COG WHEELS are used in many machines to connect different parts.

If one cog turns CLOCKWISE, the next cog will turn in the opposite direction, and so on.

WATER WHEELS capture the energy of flowing water.

The weight of water pushes the wheel around.

CONVEYOR BELTS contain lots of little wheels.

As the wheels turn, the belt moves across the top of them.

PULLEYS use wheels to make it easier to raise and lower HEAVY objects.

The wheels turn as the rope moves around them.

CONTROL WHEELS can be used to open and close VALVES inside pipes.

Usually, the control wheel is turned CLOCKWISE to close it.

This machine is designed to water plants. Scribble arrows showing which way each wheel will turn to work out which plant will get the water.

Which way do each of these cogs need to turn to open the control wheel on the pipe?

OPEN

Which way does this wheel need to turn to raise the barrier?

Which way will the water wheel turn?

Barrier

Draw the path that the water will take once the control wheel is open and the barrier is raised.

The wheels in the conveyor belt will turn in the same direction as the water wheel.

A

B

Which of the plants will be watered?

TO THE SUMMIT

Conditions on high mountains are harsh. Climbers tackling the highest summits need specialized inventions to get them to the top.

PROBLEMS CLIMBERS FACE

Slippery ice

Lack of oxygen

Extreme cold

Bad visibility/cloud

Getting lost

Falling down

Make sure your invention helps climbers tackle at least one of these problems.

DESIGN YOUR OWN mountain-climbing gear here. There are ideas for inspiration on the side of the page.

PROPELLER HAT
Warm, padded hat with attached propeller for added lift

SUCTION FEET
Extra sticking power for steep, icy slopes

HEATED SHOES
Keep toes warm and melt ice underfoot

SMART OXYGEN MASK
With low-oxygen alerts, and sensors to warn of dangers ahead

RADAR GOGGLES
With antifreeze, antifog technology, and a built-in map

AERIAL INVENTIONS

All flying machines – whether hot-air balloons, helicopters, airships, planes or rockets – depend on the same forces to fly.

A force called LIFT pushes a flying machine up into the air.

A force called THRUST pushes it forwards.

All types of aircraft must create these forces in order to fly.

AIRSHIP
Airships are filled with HELIUM gas which is lighter than air, creating lift. Propellers at the back create thrust.

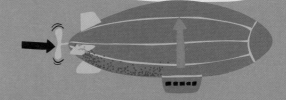

HELICOPTER
A helicopter creates lift by SPINNING blades. When the helicopter TILTS forwards, the blades also create thrust.

ROCKET
Gases are blasted out of ROCKET ENGINES, creating thrust and lift.

PLANE
PROPELLERS or JET ENGINES create thrust, pushing the plane forwards. Air flowing over the WINGS creates lift.

A smooth – or STREAMLINED – shape helps the plane move through the air more easily.

HOT-AIR BALLOON
HOT AIR is lighter than cool air. This creates lift, while blowing WIND creates thrust.

DESIGN YOUR OWN FLYING MACHINE

Hot air?

How will it create LIFT?

Helium?

Wings?

Propellers?

How will it create THRUST?

Jet engines?

Rockets?

Cockpit?

What shape will it be?

The more streamlined the shape, the less thrust it needs.

Where will the pilot sit?

Basket?

REDUCING WASTE

To help reduce the amount of waste people produce, inventions need to LAST - and need to be REUSED as often as possible.

LONGER LASTING

Many everyday items have to be replaced when children grow, or bodies change, but an ADJUSTABLE product could be used for longer...

IMAGINE your own ADJUSTABLE product here.

HOW ABOUT...

Furniture that changes height as you grow?

Shoes that extend as your feet get bigger?

Glasses with adjustable lenses to cope with changing eyesight?

REUSABLE

Lots of products are designed for SINGLE USE – to be used then thrown away. But more and more inventors are creating products that can be reused again and again, to protect the environment.

DESIGN a REUSABLE product to help people cut down on waste.

HOW ABOUT...

Rechargeable batteries with a wind-powered charger?

Batteries release toxic chemicals when thrown away, so it's best to reuse them.

Delivery box that can be reused for different size packages?

Reusable packaging cuts down on lots of waste.

IN ROMAN TIMES

The ancient Romans came up with all sorts of inventions to improve their daily lives, many of which are still in use today. Read about the Roman inventions below, then follow the instructions to complete the picture map of a city.

1 Draw a wall to surround the city.

2 CONCRETE

The Romans invented a recipe for strong concrete. The secret ingredient was VOLCANIC ASH.

Fill the city with some sturdy concrete buildings.

A forum, or public meeting place

An arena for entertainment

3 AQUEDUCTS carried water from lakes into cities.

Draw an aqueduct to supply fresh water to the city's water store.

4 ROMAN ROADS were built in straight lines, so people and goods could move as quickly as possible.

Add roads to connect places on your map.

5 SEWERS carried waste water from public baths to rivers.

Connect the public baths to a river with a sewer.

6 NEWSPAPERS

The Romans invented one of the earliest types of newspaper. News was scratched onto big stone slabs that were left in the forum for people to read.

Draw the scenes that sparked the headlines on the map below.

BREAKING NEWS
RUNAWAY CHARIOT CAUSES CHAOS

BREAKING NEWS
EMPEROR'S DOG ESCAPES CITY WALLS

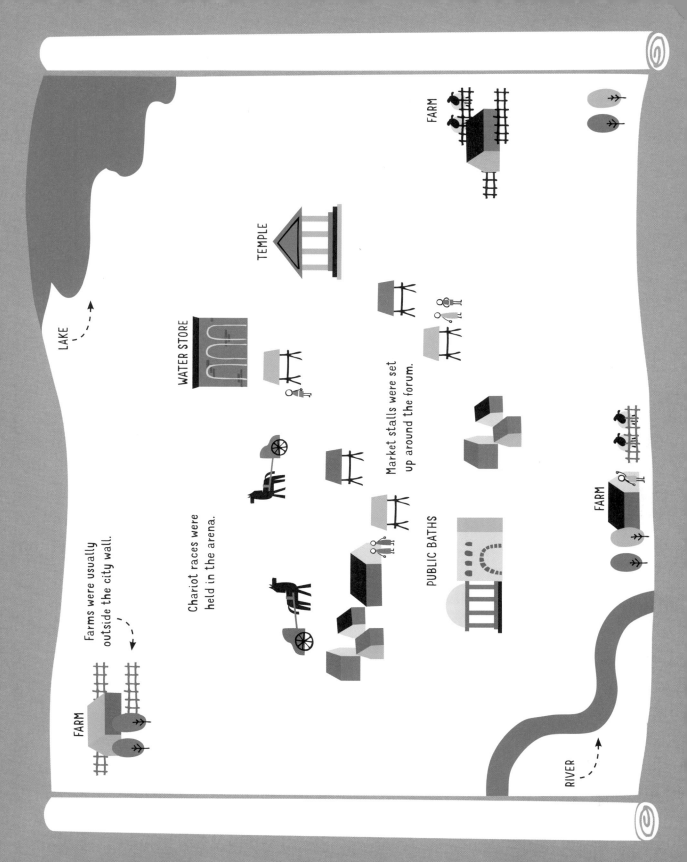

FARM

TEMPLE

LAKE

WATER STORE

Chariot races were held in the arena.

Market stalls were set up around the forum.

Farms were usually outside the city wall.

FARM

PUBLIC BATHS

FARM

RIVER

POWER CUT!

Much of the stuff people use every day is powered by electricity. But what if the electricity stopped working? Here are some ideas for inventions to replace things that normally need electricity.

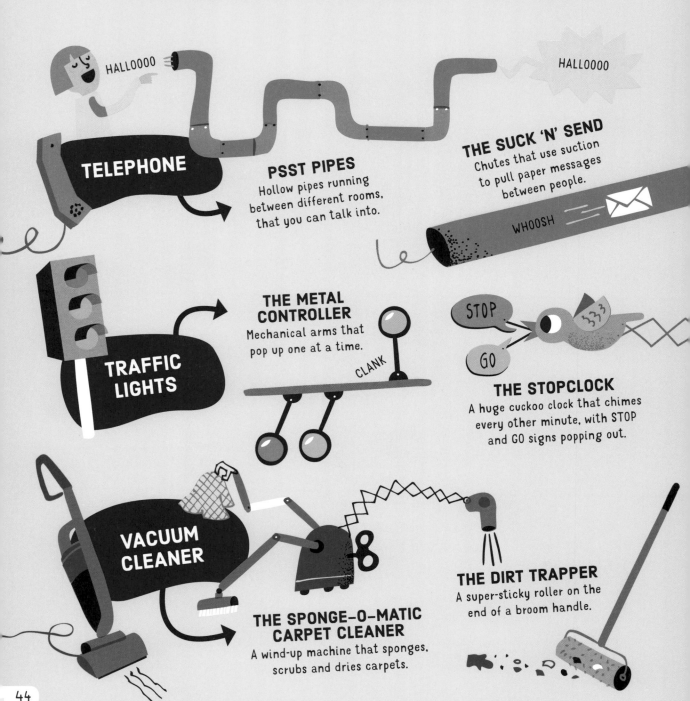

HALLOOOO

HALLOOOO

TELEPHONE

PSST PIPES
Hollow pipes running between different rooms, that you can talk into.

THE SUCK 'N' SEND
Chutes that use suction to pull paper messages between people.

WHOOSH

TRAFFIC LIGHTS

THE METAL CONTROLLER
Mechanical arms that pop up one at a time.

CLANK

STOP

GO

THE STOPCLOCK
A huge cuckoo clock that chimes every other minute, with STOP and GO signs popping out.

VACUUM CLEANER

THE SPONGE-O-MATIC CARPET CLEANER
A wind-up machine that sponges, scrubs and dries carpets.

THE DIRT TRAPPER
A super-sticky roller on the end of a broom handle.

THINK UP a device that doesn't need electricity, and describe how it might work. You could try redesigning one of the options on the right.

Twinkly lights

Hairdryer

Microphone

LEONARDO'S INVENTIONS

A 15th-century Italian inventor and artist named LEONARDO DA VINCI came up with ideas for hundreds of new inventions. Many of his designs are strikingly similar to modern inventions that were created relatively recently.

Draw lines to match up the replica of Leonardo's sketch with the name he gave his invention and the modern invention that followed.

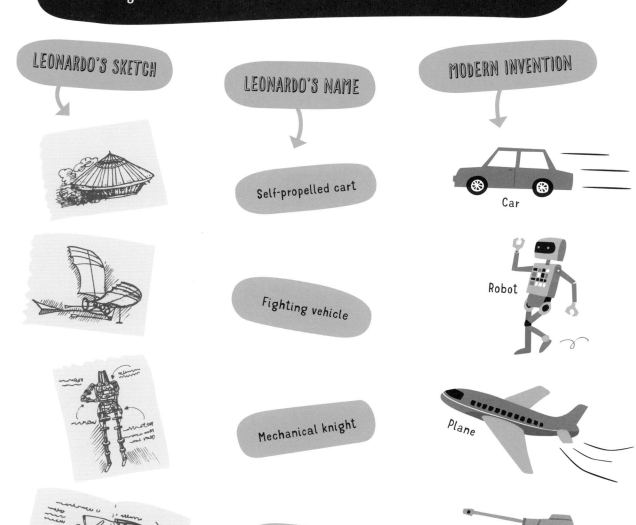

LEONARDO'S SKETCH

LEONARDO'S NAME

MODERN INVENTION

Self-propelled cart

Fighting vehicle

Mechanical knight

Flying machine

Car

Robot

Plane

Tank

INVENT YOUR OWN ROBOT

Increasingly, robots are being used for all sorts of tasks, from working in factories to exploring space.

Invent a robot that could help and entertain you.

A human?

What does it look like?

A pet?

What can it do?

Play sports or games?

$(10 \div 2) \times 5 = 25$

Once upon a time...

Answer questions about homework?

Tell stories?

BUILD A PROTOTYPE

Once an invention has been designed, the next step is to build a model of it. This is called a PROTOTYPE.

Design a prototype of a box that can be reused as something else once empty. Here are some ideas.

A box of model blocks that unfolds to make a map to build on

A box of toy cars that unfolds to make a ramp

A box of candy snakes with a snakes and ladders game inside it

BLOCKS

CARS

gummm SSSNAKES

INSIDE

Scribble some ideas here.

IDEAS

BOX

Now build your prototype.

Once you're happy with your design, build a prototype using the template opposite.

Copy the template opposite, or download it from the Usborne QUICKLINKS website.

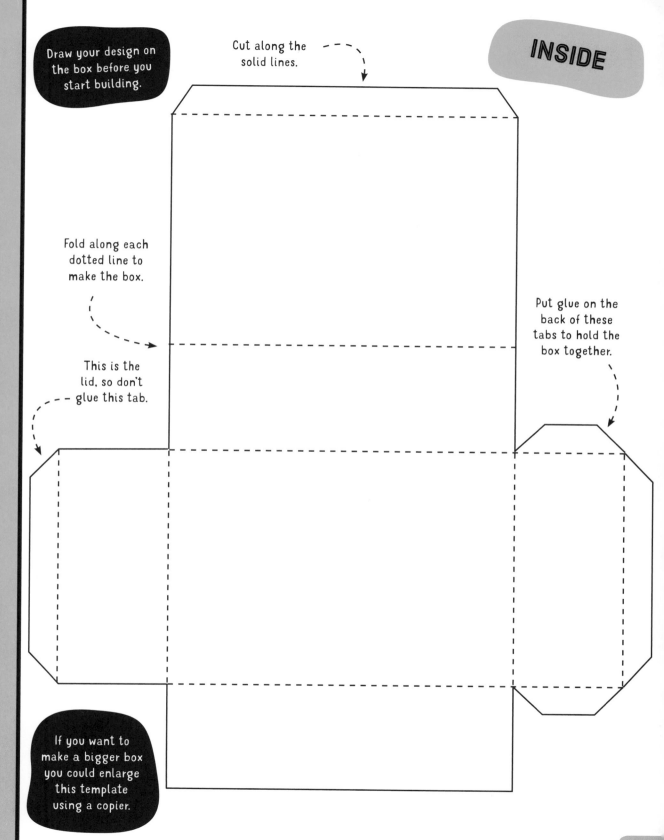

Draw your design on the box before you start building.

Cut along the solid lines.

INSIDE

Fold along each dotted line to make the box.

This is the lid, so don't glue this tab.

Put glue on the back of these tabs to hold the box together.

If you want to make a bigger box you could enlarge this template using a copier.

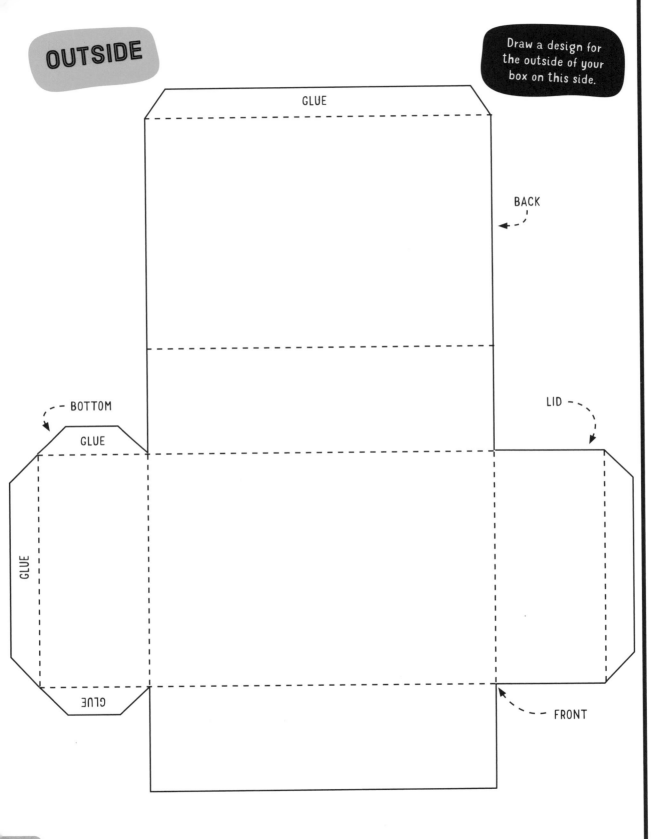

OUTSIDE

Draw a design for the outside of your box on this side.

GLUE

BACK

BOTTOM

LID

GLUE

GLUE

GLUE

FRONT

ACCIDENTAL INVENTIONS

Some inventions were made by accident. Match each story to the invention that came from it, by putting a number in each box.

SUPER GLUE

MICROWAVE OVEN

GLASS

ICE-CREAM CONE

BUBBLE WRAP

1
A scientist named Percy Spencer realized the chocolate in his pocket melted when he got close to some machines in his lab...

2
American engineers created wallpaper with air pockets. It didn't make good wallpaper, but it was great for something else...

3
5,000 years ago, some Syrian sailors had a blazing fire on a beach. They left it overnight and, in the morning, the sand had transformed...

4
While trying to create a new chemical, scientist Harry Coover invented a substance that stuck stuff in his lab together VERY firmly...

5
In the 1900s, a street food seller ran out of dishes, so began using waffles...

ON YOUR MARKS...

Sports and games are inventions too.
Follow the steps to invent your own.

What's the aim of your game? Jot your ideas below.

To get a ball in a goal?

 To outwit an opponent?

 To score points?

To win a race?

What equipment does it need? Draw it here.

Bats, balls or counters?

Nets, goals or boards?

How many players are there?
Do they play in teams?
Draw them here.

Where will it be played?

Is there a playing area, field or court?

What shape is the playing area?

Circular

Rectangular

Triangular

What is it made from?

Grass

Ice

Clay

What will you call your game?

The name 'chess' comes from the Persian word 'shah', which means king.

Rugby is named after Rugby School in England, where the sport was first played.

WHOOOSH

Some names describe how the game works, such as long jump and basketball.

FIZZLE & FLASH

Fireworks were invented in China over a thousand years ago.
Since then, the original design has been refined and developed
to create all sorts of shades and patterns in the sky.

LIFT OFF
The bottom of a firework is
packed with gunpowder.

When the gunpowder is set
alight, it releases a stream
of hot gases, pushing the
firework up into the sky.

The MORE gunpowder
there is, the HIGHER
the firework will soar.

Fireworks are filled with balls of explosive powder, known as STARS.
When the firework explodes in mid-air, the stars burn
brightly and spread across the sky.

DIFFERENT SHADES
The stars contain powdered metals.
When these burn they create different shades.

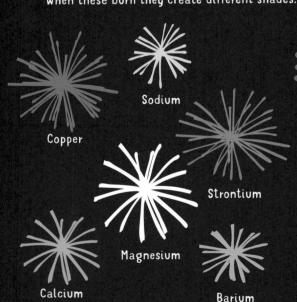

Copper

Sodium

Strontium

Magnesium

Calcium

Barium

MAKING PATTERNS
Stars are put on a piece of cardboard
inside the firework. The pattern that the
stars make on the cardboard is the same
as the pattern they will make in the sky.

IMAGINE three new fireworks. Draw them as they explode in the sky below. Then write out information for each firework in the boxes at the bottom.

Which metals would each firework need to produce the shade you want?

How would the stars need to be arranged to make your pattern in the sky?

Which of your fireworks would need the most gunpowder?

NAME:_ _ _ _ _ _ _ _ _ _ _

SHADE:_ _ _ _ _ _ _ _ _ _

METAL:_ _ _ _ _ _ _ _ _ _

PATTERN:

NAME:_ _ _ _ _ _ _ _ _ _ _

SHADE:_ _ _ _ _ _ _ _ _ _

METAL:_ _ _ _ _ _ _ _ _ _

PATTERN:

NAME:_ _ _ _ _ _ _ _ _ _ _

SHADE:_ _ _ _ _ _ _ _ _ _

METAL:_ _ _ _ _ _ _ _ _ _

PATTERN:

MULTIPURPOSE INVENTIONS

To save space or reduce waste,
it can be useful if an invention serves
SEVERAL DIFFERENT PURPOSES.

DESIGN an invention that can TRANSFORM from one thing into another, and back again. There are some ideas around the page to help.

BEFORE

What two jobs does your invention do?

How does it transform from one thing to the other?

You could add parts that...

ATTACH

FOLD

CLIP

INFLATE

EXTEND

AFTER

Hood FOLDS over to
close the bag.

Sleeves CLIP down to
become straps.

The bottom ZIPS
closed so the bag
can be filled.

A CHAIR that becomes a BED

Wheels ILLUMINATE
as night lights.

Seat INFLATES to
become a pillow.

Back UNFOLDS to
make a mattress.

MAKING DO

Sometimes inventors have to make do with limited resources. [An] explosion onboard one early moon mission meant scientists on Earth [had] to invent a way for astronauts to deal with the damage using just a few simple materials, such as tape, plastic bags and socks.

[What] could you create using [ju]st these five materials?

Cans

Rubber bands

Pencils

Cardboard box

Balloons

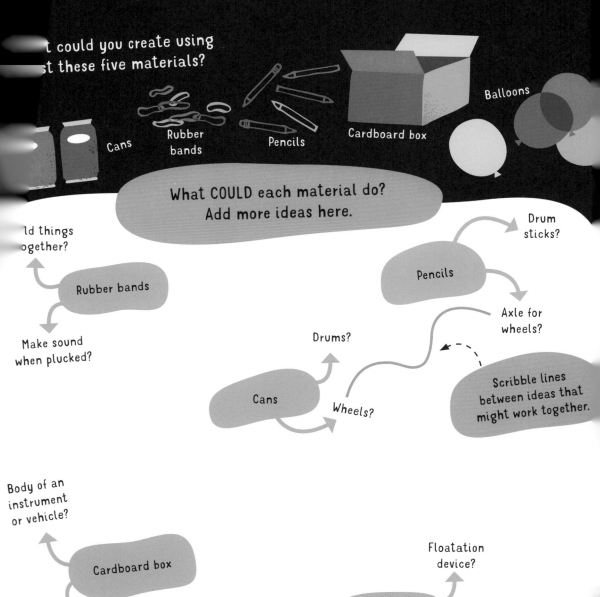

What COULD each material do?
Add more ideas here.

[Ho]ld things [t]ogether?

Rubber bands

Make sound when plucked?

Drum sticks?

Pencils

Axle for wheels?

Drums?

Cans

Wheels?

Scribble lines between ideas that might work together.

Body of an instrument or vehicle?

Cardboard box

Shelter?

Floatation device?

Balloons

Water container?

DESIGN your invention here.
Add labels to show what each part does.

HOW ABOUT...

...AN AIR-POWERED VEHICLE?

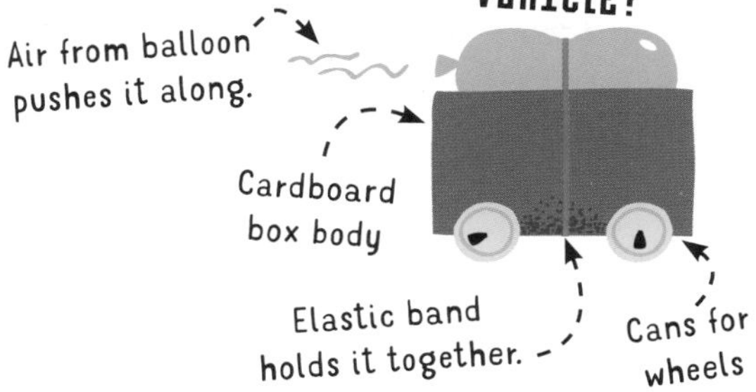

Air from balloon pushes it along.

Cardboard box body

Elastic band holds it together.

Cans for wheels

...A FLOATING DELIVERY DEVICE?

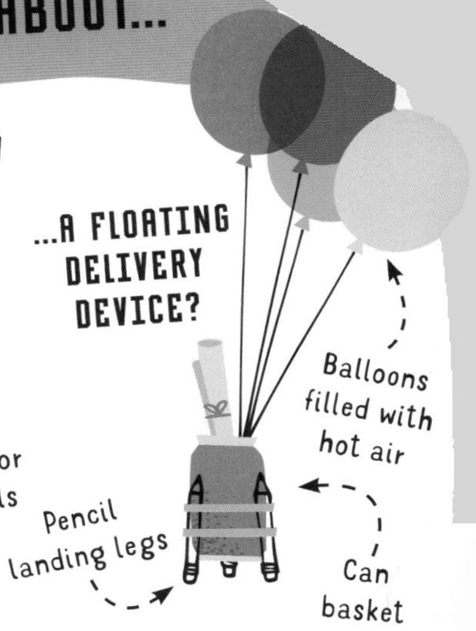

Balloons filled with hot air

Pencil landing legs

Can basket

GIVE YOUR INVENTION A NAME:

IMPOSSIBLE INVENTIONS

Occasionally a new idea comes along that seems impossible at the time, but becomes possible later. Here are some famous inventions that people used to think were impossible...

THEN...

...AND NOW

PERSONAL COMPUTERS

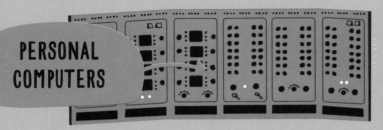

In the 1940s, computers filled whole rooms and could only do a limited range of tasks. There was no way, at that time, to make them smaller or more powerful.

Today new computer chips make it possible for many people to own a small, powerful computer.

TELEVISIONS

SQUIRREL FINDS LARGEST ACORN

The first television was invented in the 1920s. It worked, but it wasn't possible to make in large numbers.

Now new manufacturing methods mean there's one in almost every household.

HOVERBOARDS

For many years, hoverboards were found only in sci-fi books and movies...

...but today 'hoverboards' like this are for sale all over the world.

IMAGINE another impossible invention.
You never know - maybe someday in
the future everyone will have one.

HOW ABOUT...

ANTI-GRAVITY shoes

A device to
CONTROL THE
WEATHER

An INSTANT-TRANSPORTATION
machine

UPGRADE AN INVENTION

Inventors don't always create something new – often they just IMPROVE something that already exists. For example, steam trains were replaced with more powerful diesel trains, then more environmentally friendly electric trains.

CAN I MAKE IT...

...SAFER?   ...CHEAPER?   ...MORE ENVIRONMENTALLY FRIENDLY?

...EASIER TO USE?   ...FASTER?

Think of ways to improve these inventions.

REFRIGERATOR

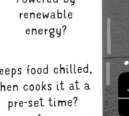

Reminds you when food is going bad?

Powered by renewable energy?

Keeps food chilled, then cooks it at a pre-set time?

BICYCLE

Battery to store energy from pedalling and braking?

Hand-warmers built in to the handlebars?

Airbag to break the rider's fall if there's a crash?

CAR

Fold-out wings so it can fly?

Robotic driver?

Floats and a propeller so it can travel across water?

Improve one of your own inventions from somewhere in the book.

ORIGINAL INVENTION:

WHAT'S THE POINT?

Most inventions are created to SOLVE PROBLEMS.
But not all have to be useful. Some are just for fun...

Use this space to come up with your own pointless but fun invention.

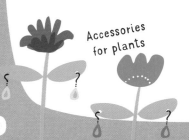
Accessories for plants

Pet wigs

Worm umbrella

GIVE IT A NAME

Every good invention needs a memorable name.

Add words to the mindmaps to come up with a name for each invention.

SELF-CLEANING SHOES

Shiny

Sparkly

New

NAME: Good as New Shiny Shoe

Catchy names often rhyme or repeat the same first letter. Simple is best.

Catch

Bounce

Return

A BALL THAT AUTOMATICALLY RETURNS TO ITS OWNER

NAME:

Non-stop

Forever

Always

A PHONE THAT NEVER RUNS OUT OF BATTERY POWER

NAME:

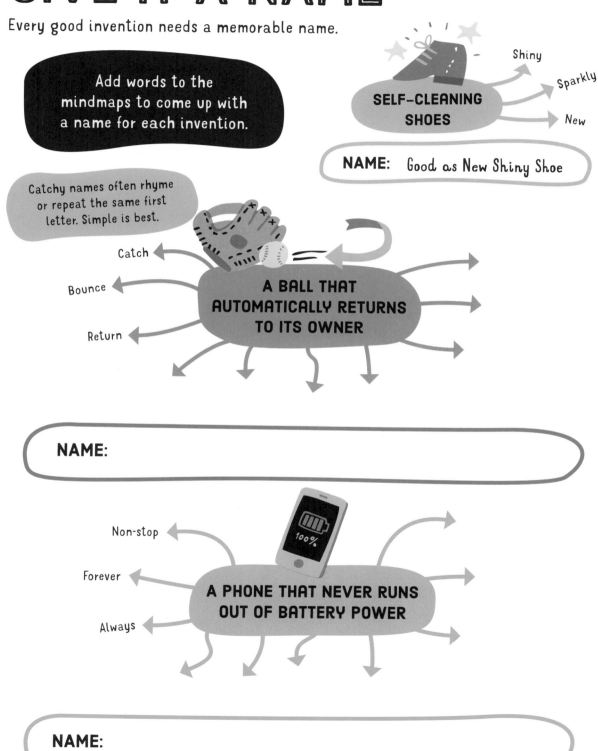

MANY MINDS

Most everyday items aren't invented by a single person. They're a combination of ideas from different people. Take the examples below. Work out which inventors helped to create each one, then write the numbers in the boxes.

1. CAMERAS

2. WINDSHIELD WIPERS

3. POTATO SNACKS

In 1978, I invented a way to improve the quality of photos, using radioactive materials. It's especially useful for photos taken in space.

In 1903, I patented a rubber blade that people could move by hand to see clearly while driving.

GEORGE CRUM

In 1853, I developed a popular snack by thinly slicing and frying potatoes.

BARBARA ASKINS

MARY ANDERSON

ROBERT KEARNS

In 1964, I helped drivers to see better in light rain by inventing a way to control how often rubber blades move.

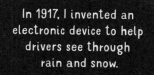
In 1917, I invented an electronic device to help drivers see through rain and snow.

CHARLOTTE BRIDGWOOD

WILLIAM HENRY FOX TALBOT

In the 1830s, I invented a way of leaving a permanent image on a piece of paper by shining light onto it for a few minutes.

In the 11th century, I built a dark room in which light captured from the outside could be used to produce an image.

LAURA SCUDDER

In the 1830s I invented a way to make images on chemical-coated sheets of copper.

IBN AL-HAYTHAM

In 1926, I invented a way of sealing food in wax paper bags to keep it fresh.

LOUIS DAGUERRE

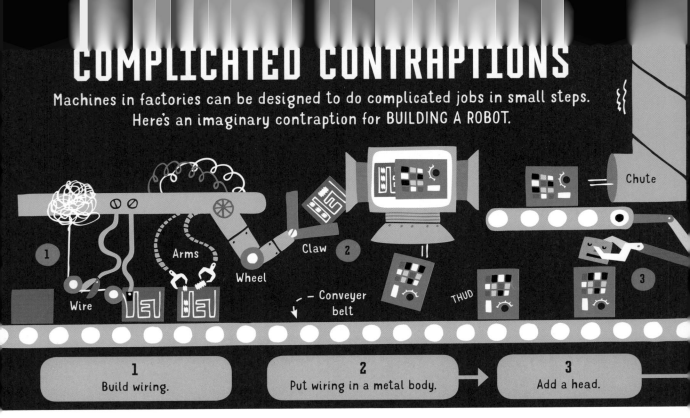

COMPLICATED CONTRAPTIONS

Machines in factories can be designed to do complicated jobs in small steps.
Here's an imaginary contraption for BUILDING A ROBOT.

Chute

1

Arms

Claw

2

Wheel

Wire

Conveyer belt

THUD

3

1	2	3
Build wiring.	Put wiring in a metal body.	Add a head.

Design your own contraption.
Break the job down into steps, and add
a part for each step.

YOU COULD CREATE
A MACHINE TO...

...MAKE A CAKE.

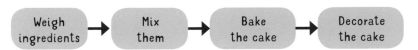

Weigh ingredients → Mix them → Bake the cake → Decorate the cake

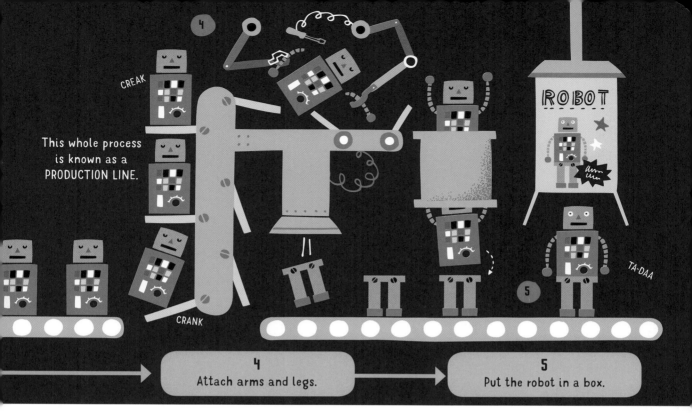

This whole process is known as a PRODUCTION LINE.

CREAK

CRANK

ROBOT

TA-DAA

4
Attach arms and legs.

5
Put the robot in a box.

...GET YOU READY IN THE MORNING.

Wake you up → Give you a wash → Put your clothes on → Make you breakfast

PUZZLING INVENTIONS

All sorts of puzzles have been invented to keep people entertained.
Try solving these invention-themed puzzles.

Fill in the crossword using the clues
and the rest of the book to help you.

ACROSS:

3. First name of famous
15th-century Italian inventor (8)

4. Invented by the Romans to
move water into cities (8)

6. Device that uses wheels to
raise and lower heavy objects (6)

8. Force that pushes flying
machines up into the air (4)

10. Turn waste into something new,
instead of throwing it away (7)

11. Name of model made once
an invention is designed (9)

DOWN:

1. Explosive invention that makes
bright patterns in the night sky (8)

2. Invention designed
to make music (10)

4. A computer program
that runs on a phone (3)

5. Name often used for a
technical drawing (9)

6. Legal document that says
who owns an invention (6)

7. Accidental invention used to
make cups and windows (5)

9. Flying machine with wings (5)

Crosswords were developed from an
earlier puzzle known as a WORD SQUARE.
The first crossword was published
in the US in 1913.

Originally called 'word-cross', a
printing error led to the name
'crossword', which quickly caught on.

Fill in the grid with these four inventions. Each row, column, and 4-square box must contain one of each.

Pencil

Battery

Phone

Wheel

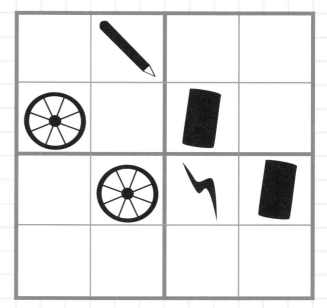

One of the most common types of grid puzzles is known as Sudoku. Invented in 1979, it usually involves using numbers 1-9.

Find all ten words below to solve this wordsearch.

LOGO   REUSE

SLOGAN   DESIGN

WHEEL   COG

CONTRAPTION   MACHINE

GADGET   ROBOT

The largest wordsearch ever invented contains 10,500 words in a grid filled with more than 120,000 letters.

D	B	G	C	C	R	U	Q	R	O	B	O	T	Y
N	F	C	O	N	T	R	A	P	T	I	O	N	E
L	Q	E	G	U	I	D	Z	N	Q	F	C	F	R
H	R	A	F	P	R	V	L	O	G	O	W	I	V
B	M	K	W	M	C	A	E	P	X	G	E	U	S
D	J	A	B	D	F	G	W	H	E	E	L	V	L
O	Y	B	C	S	E	D	U	F	R	H	R	D	O
C	B	C	A	H	X	S	Y	D	G	O	H	U	G
A	R	Z	G	Q	I	B	I	A	J	I	R	I	A
O	E	T	A	H	A	N	D	G	P	D	X	K	N
P	U	E	D	D	L	Z	E	Y	N	I	H	P	O
I	S	Z	G	T	E	M	O	E	I	Y	S	B	X
M	E	J	E	O	N	L	N	M	J	L	P	K	W
W	O	I	T	N	M	T	D	K	Q	T	U	E	J

SELL IT!

Once you've come up with a great invention, you need to persuade people to buy it. This is known as MARKETING.

Take an invention you've created and use these steps to sell it to the world.

First of all, draw your invention out here.

Here's an example for the pet wig invention on page 64.

Now give it a name.

Fancy Furstyles

Create a LOGO.
The logo could include the invention's name or its initials, or just be an image.

Logos should be simple, easily recognizable, and represent the invention in some way.

Come up with a catchy SLOGAN.
The best slogans are snappy and easy to remember.

For the pet who has everything.

Use this space to create an ADVERTISEMENT for your invention. Start by writing the NAME in big letters to stand out. Then, add the LOGO, SLOGAN and anything else you want.

FF FANCY FURSTYLES

For the pet who has everything.

WHY DO INVENTIONS MATTER?

It's easy to forget how important some inventions are.
But if they didn't exist, life would be very different...

If an invention on this page was taken away, which one would you find it hardest to live without?

Planes?

Computers?

Cars?

Smart phones?

Books?

Glasses?

Bikes?

Wheels?

BOING

Pogo stick?

Light bulbs?

Clocks?

Shoes?

What makes a GREAT invention?

Does it CHANGE THE WORLD?

Does it HELP PEOPLE?

Does it make its inventor RICH?

Is it something you CAN'T LIVE WITHOUT?

Based on your notes above, which of YOUR inventions in this book is the GREATEST?

MY GREATEST INVENTION:

IT'S THE GREATEST BECAUSE:

MAKE IT YOURS

When inventors come up with something new, they apply for a document known as a PATENT. This says the invention LEGALLY belongs to the inventor, so no one else can copy it and claim it as theirs. Here's how the patent process works.

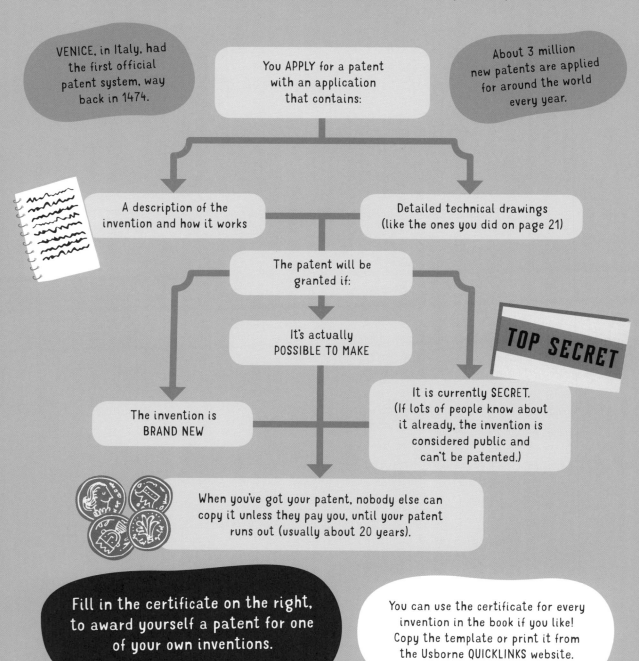

VENICE, in Italy, had the first official patent system, way back in 1474.

You APPLY for a patent with an application that contains:

About 3 million new patents are applied for around the world every year.

A description of the invention and how it works

Detailed technical drawings (like the ones you did on page 21)

The patent will be granted if:

It's actually POSSIBLE TO MAKE

TOP SECRET

The invention is BRAND NEW

It is currently SECRET. (If lots of people know about it already, the invention is considered public and can't be patented.)

When you've got your patent, nobody else can copy it unless they pay you, until your patent runs out (usually about 20 years).

Fill in the certificate on the right, to award yourself a patent for one of your own inventions.

You can use the certificate for every invention in the book if you like! Copy the template or print it from the Usborne QUICKLINKS website.

PATENT
CERTIFICATE

CERTIFICATE AWARDED TO: _____

FOR THE INVENTION: _____

DATE: _____

SIGNED: _____ Scribble Official

SIGNED: _____ Inventor (YOU!)

16 FROM FICTION TO REALITY

 **1.** IN-EAR EARPHONES

 **2.** SMARTWATCH

 **3.** CREDIT CARD

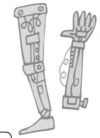 **4.** BIONIC LIMBS

35 WORKING WITH WHEELS

Plant B gets watered.

A   B

46 LEONARDO'S INVENTIONS

Fighting vehicle
Tank

Flying machine
Plane

Mechanical knight
Robot

Self-propelled cart
Car

51 ACCIDENTAL INVENTIONS

 4 **1**

SUPER GLUE MICROWAVE OVEN

3 **5** **2**

GLASS ICE-CREAM CONE BUBBLE WRAP

66-67 MANY MINDS

1. CAMERAS
Ibn al-Haytham
Louis Daguerre
William Henry Fox Talbot
Barbara Askins

2. WINDSHIELD WIPERS
Mary Anderson
Charlotte Bridgwood
Robert Kearns

3. POTATO SNACKS
George Crum
Laura Scudder

70-71 PUZZLING INVENTIONS

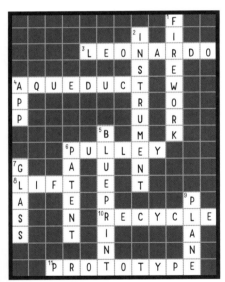

First published in 2020 by Usborne Publishing Ltd., Usborne House, 83-85 Saffron Hill, London EC1N 8RT, England.
Usborne.com Copyright © 2020 Usborne Publishing Ltd.